THE
VANISHING
MOUSTACHE

Mr. Fulves is standing on the shore of a lake, watching the bathers. In the last picture on the front cover of this book, it looks as if Mr. Fulves' moustache has mysteriously disappeared. Can you explain what happened?

You will find the answer to this puzzle on page 99—and there are many more clever and diverting mind-teasers in this collection selected for your enjoyment by Martin Gardner.

About the Author and Illustrator:

MARTIN GARDNER has written the "Mathematical Games" column in *Scientific American* since 1957 and for nine years was contributing editor for *Humpty Dumpty's Magazine*. He is the author of a number of books for adults (*Mathematical Puzzles and Diversions, The Annotated Alice, Relativity for the Million, The Numerology of Dr. Matrix*) and for young readers (*Mathematical Puzzles, Science Puzzlers*), including a book of cautionary verse for children, *Never Make Fun of a Turtle, My Son*. Mr. Gardner, whose principal hobby is conjuring, now lives with his wife in Hastings-on-Hudson, New York. *Perplexing Puzzles and Tantalizing Teasers* is also available in an Archway Paperback edition.

LASZLO KUBINYI has studied art at the Boston Museum School, the School of Visual Arts, and the Art Students League in New York City. He grew up on Cape Ann, Massachusetts, and has traveled throughout the world, particularly in the Middle East. Now living in New York City with his wife Suzanne, Mr. Kubinyi divides his time between illustrating children's books and playing the *dumbek*, a Middle Eastern drum, in an Armenian orchestra.

MORE PERPLEXING PUZZLES and TANTALIZING TEASERS

by
Martin Gardner

Illustrated by
Laszlo Kubinyi

AN ARCHWAY PAPERBACK
POCKET BOOKS • NEW YORK

MORE PERPLEXING PUZZLES AND
TANTALIZING TEASERS

Archway Paperback edition published November, 1977

Published by
POCKET BOOKS, a Simon & Schuster Division of
GULF & WESTERN CORPORATION
1230 Avenue of the Americas, New York, N.Y. 10020.

Archway Paperback editions are distributed in the U.S. by
Simon & Schuster, Inc., 1230 Avenue of the Americas,
New York, N.Y. 10020, and in Canada by Simon & Schuster
of Canada, Ltd., Richmond Hill, Ontario, Canada.

ISBN: 0-671-29832-1.

1287

For my grand-nephew
Bobby Schoeppel

Contents

Introduction

Dear Friend:

This book is a sequel to *Perplexing Puzzles and Tantalizing Teasers*. The same artist who illustrated that book, Mr. Laszlo Kubinyi, has illustrated this one. Don't you agree that he has caught the spirit of the puzzles and done a marvelous job?

If you liked the previous book, you are sure to like this one. Its puzzles are on the same level of difficulty, and they have been carefully selected to exercise your brain in a way that I guarantee you won't find boring. The solutions are at the back of the book. I can't stop you from peeking at those answers, but I can tell you that, if you resist the temptation until you've tried as hard as you can to solve a puzzle, you'll get much more pleasure from the book.

Please write to me, in care of the publishers, if you have any good ideas for new puzzles, or to tell me which puzzles you liked best.

Martin Gardner

MORE
PERPLEXING
PUZZLES
and
TANTALIZING
TEASERS

1

Ten Ridiculous Riddles

1. What does a duck do when it flies upside down?

2. If all cars in the United States were pink, what kind of flower would the United States be?

3. How do you keep a skunk from smelling?

4. What did George Washington say to his men before they got in their boat to cross the Delaware?

5. Why does Tony the fireman have red suspenders?

6. What's big, green, and loves hot tamales?

7. Where do vampires get their mail?

8. What's Smokey the Bear's middle name?

9. What do you get when you cross a hippo with a jar of peanut butter?

10. What's gray, has four legs, a tail, and a trunk?

2

Fat Bats and Other Funny Beasts

Each picture shows an animal that can be described by two words that rhyme. Two examples are given. Can you find a rhyming pair of words for the other animals?

Fat bat

Cryin' lion

3

"The Whistler"

Mr. and Mrs. Smith have a son who is an artist. He has just sent them a painting. In a letter he said that the picture's title is "The Whistler."

Mr. and Mrs. Smith are puzzled. All they can see is a circle and four spots. Why in the world did their son call it "The Whistler"? And what does that label "68 ON" mean?

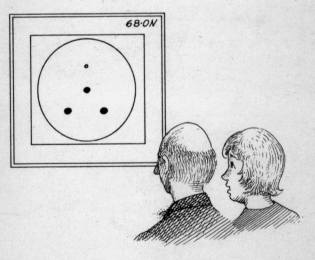

4
Where Does the Ball Go?

Keep your eyes on that tiny "x" between the tennis ball and the boy's face. Then bring the page slowly toward the tip of your nose. You'll see the ball fly straight into the boy's mouth!

5

Tricky Questions

Speedy Retirement

Bascom turned off the light in his bedroom
and was able to get to bed before the room was
dark. His bed is 15 feet from the wall switch.
How did Bascom do it?

Peculiar Word

What familiar word starts with IS, ends with
AND, and has LA in the middle?

Mystery Ball

How can you throw a ball so it goes a short
distance, comes to a dead stop, reverses its mo-
tion, then goes the opposite way? You are not
allowed to bounce it off anything, hit it with
anything, or tie anything to it.

Shrewd Barbers

Why do barbers in Los Angeles prefer cutting the hair of ten fat men to cutting the hair
of one skinny man?

6

What Do You Do Next?

Here are a dozen funny jokes to play on friends. In every case the joke is doing something your friends don't expect. Pretend you are playing these jokes on someone. See if you can guess what you are supposed to do after your friends respond to your first remark.

1. Did you know I can stick out my tongue and touch my nose?

2. Brush the back of your hand lightly down over a person's face, from forehead to chin, and say, "Did you like that?"

3. Do you know how to make an ordinary pencil, with black lead, write red or blue?

4. Put the palm of your right hand on top of your left fist, and then say "wing" three times.

5. Hand me your plate and I'll show you how to push it through the handle of my cup.

6. I can drop this paper match on the table so it will land on its *edge* and stay there.

7. I can have you and a friend stand on the same sheet of newspaper in such a way that neither of you can touch the other.

8. Would you like to see me crawl into a pill bottle?

9. Would you like to have your palm read?

10. Ever see a match burn underwater?

11. What's sexy and hums?

12. Do you know how to keep an idiot in suspense?

7

The Musicians of Inviz

Inviz is one of the strangest of all villages in Oz. Every day in Inviz all objects of a certain type become invisible. The pictures show what happened on the day that no one could see a musical instrument. Your task is to guess what instrument is being played by each musician. (See art on pp. 10-11).

8

To Be or Not to Be

There are at least 89 things in this picture with names that begin with the letter B. How many can you find?

9

What's the Difference?

The picture on the right page shows the same scene as the picture on the left, except it has been reflected in a mirror. Aside from that, however,

the two pictures are not exactly alike. If you look carefully, you'll find six spots where things are not the same. Can you find all six?

10

Easy as ABC

1. The design below is for a Christmas card. What single-word Christmas greeting does it convey?

A	B	C	D	E
F	G	H	I	J
K	M	N	O	P
Q	R	S	T	U
V	W	X	Y	Z

2. The artist has divided all capital letters into two groups: those on the line and those dropped below the line. On what basis did he make the division?

A EF HI KLMN   T VWXYZ
 BCD G J   OPQRS U

3. The word "moon" can be formed by using letters next to one another in the alphabet as shown by the bracket. How many dictionary words can you form by using adjacent letters? We won't count the obvious single-letter words "a" and "I," or easy two-letter words such as "hi," "on," and "no." There are more than 20 words of three or more letters that you can make, most of them familiar words. Remember, a letter can be used more than once, but all the letters must be next to one another in the alphabet.

MOON

ABCDEFGHIJKL M N O PQRSTUVWXYZ

Four Eye Twiddlers

The Two Spirals

One of these spirals is formed with a single piece of rope that has its ends joined. The other is formed with two separate pieces of rope, each with joined ends. Can you tell which is which by using only your eyes? No fair tracing the lines with a pencil.

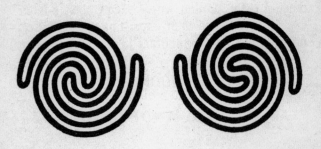

The Ghost Triangle

Doesn't it look as if a white triangle is pasted on the page? The white triangle is an illusion. It isn't there at all.

Trap the Beetle

The beetle seems to be on the outside of the box. But stare at the box for a minute or two and something strange will happen. It sort of turns inside out and you'll see the beetle on the *inside*, on a checked floor of the box.

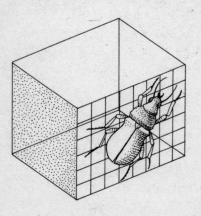

The Curious Cube

There are two spots in this picture where a pair of line segments meet at right angles. Can you find them? You can prove they are right angles by fitting the corner of a sheet of paper into them.

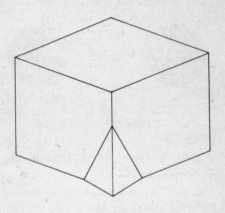

12

Dividing the Cake

One large piece of cake is to be shared between Henry and his sister Henrietta. The two are squabbling over who gets to cut the cake. Each thinks the other will cut it so as to give himself or herself the larger portion.

Dad let them argue for a while before he said, "May I make a suggestion? I'll show you how to decide the matter so both of you will be completely satisfied with your share."

When Henry and Henrietta heard Dad's clever scheme, they agreed it would work. What did Dad suggest?

13

Find the Mistakes

The artist has made 27 mistakes in this picture, but some are not easy to find. For instance, the keyhole in the door is upside down. See how quickly you can spot the others.

14

Three Match Puzzles

1. Arrange four paper matches as shown.
Move just one match to make a square.

2. Nine matches make the equation below. The numbers are in Roman numerals. The equation is wrong because 1 minus 3 does *not* equal 2. Move just one match to correct the equation.

3. Here's another equation of Roman numerals, made with ten matches. It, too, is incorrect. Can you correct the equation without touching the matches, adding new matches, or taking away any matches?

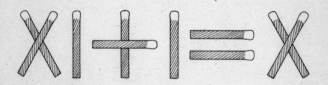

15

Help Sherlock Catch the Criminals

Sherlock Holmes is looking for a man and a woman who are wanted by the police. He's been told they are somewhere in this airline terminal, pretending not to know each other. The man is clean shaven, with dark hair, no glasses, a bowtie and a light-colored suit. The lady is a blonde, wearing a scarf and glasses, and carrying a light-colored shoulder bag. How quickly can you find them?

16

The Two Watering Cans

A woman is trying to decide which of the two watering cans to buy. She wants the one that holds the most water. Which one do you recommend?

See Sherman Shave

Sheldon Sherman has been on a fishing trip and hasn't shaved for five days. Here you see him halfway through shaving.

To see how Sheldon looked *before* he started shaving, place the edge of a mirror on the dotted line and look into the mirror from the left.

To see how Sheldon will look *after* he finishes shaving, turn the mirror around, put it back on the dotted line, and look into it from the right.

18
Find the Duck

The rabbit is chasing a duck. Where's the duck?

Three-letter Word

In your mind, move the three arrows so they point to three letters that, taken left to right, spell a familiar word.

Four More Eye Twiddlers

The Bulgy Balloon
   Is the balloon a perfect circle?

Two Men on a Cliff

One of these men must be suspended in mid-air, but which one?

Find the Center

Which dot is the true center of this circle? Take a guess before you make any measurements.

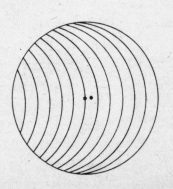

Spooky Spots

Do you see little gray spots at the intersections of the white lines between the black squares? When you try to look directly at a spot, it vanishes!

A Pair of Ants

On each of these twisted paper strips are two ants crawling in the directions shown by the arrows. If they keep on going in the same direction, and never cross an edge of the strip, will either pair ever meet head-on?

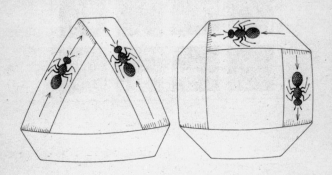

What Do You Say Next?

These are catches like the ones in the previous puzzle called "What Do You Do Next?," except that now it's what you *say* next that is the joke. Before you look at the answers, see if you can anticipate the joke and guess what you're supposed to say.

1. YOU: Did you know I have ESP? Go across the room, write any word on a piece of paper, fold it, put it under your left foot, and I'll tell you what's on the paper.

FRIEND: Okay, it's done. What's on the paper?

2. YOU: T-O, T-O-O, and T-W-O are all pronounced the same way. How do you pronounce the second day of the week?

FRIEND: Tuesday.

3. YOU: Ice in water makes iced water. What does ice in ink make?

FRIEND: Iced ink.

4. YOU: Touch your head and say the two letters for the abbreviation for "mountain."
FRIEND: M.T.

5. YOU: What's the difference between a mailbox and a garbage can?
FRIEND: I don't know.

6. YOU: If you asked your mother to put a stamp on an envelope and she refused, what would you do?
FRIEND: I'd put it on myself.

7. YOU: There's nothing I love to eat more than updock.
FRIEND: What's updock?

8. YOU: Just imagine! Getting up in the middle of the night to go horseback riding!
FRIEND: Who did that?

9. YOU: Seven times 8 is 54. Will you give me a dollar if I'm wrong?
FRIEND: Sure.

10. YOU: Suppose you're standing in line to buy an airplane ticket. The man in front of you is flying to London. The lady behind you is flying to Paris. Where are *you* going?
FRIEND: I give up.

11. YOU: It's running down my back!
FRIEND: What is?

12. YOU: Can you say "I one a bug, I two a bug, I three a bug," and so on, up through number eight?
FRIEND: I one a bug, I two a bug, I three a bug, I four a bug, I five a bug, I six a bug, I seven a bug, I eight a bug.

Mysterious Hieroglyphics

What do these strange symbols mean?

24

Tricky Mysteries

Murder at the Ski Resort

A Chicago lawyer and his wife went to Switzerland for a vacation. While they were skiing in the Alps, the wife skidded over a precipice and was killed. Back in Chicago an airline clerk read about the accident and immediately phoned the police. The lawyer was arrested and tried for murder.

The clerk did not know the lawyer or his wife. Nothing he'd heard or seen made him suspect foul play until he read about the accident in the paper. Why did he call the police?

Funny Business at the Fountain

At a hotel in Las Vegas, a lady rushed out of the manager's office to get a long drink at the water fountain in the lobby. A few minutes later she came out for another drink. This time she was followed by a man.

There was a mirror behind the fountain. When the lady raised her head, she saw that the man behind her had a knife in his upraised fist. She screamed.

The man lowered his knife, and then both of them began to laugh. What on earth is going on?

Accident on the Thruway

Mr. Jones was driving along the thruway with his son in the front seat. The road was icy. When Mr. Jones rounded a curve, his car skidded and rammed into a telephone pole. Mr. Jones was unhurt, but the boy broke several ribs.

An ambulance took the boy to the nearest hospital. He was wheeled into the emergency operating room. The surgeon took one look at the patient and said, "I can't operate on this boy. He's my son!"

How could this be?

25

Bee on the Nose

A bee has just landed on the girl's nose. Put a mirror's edge on the dotted line and look into it from the left to see how the girl looked a moment later.

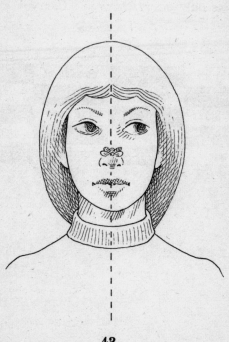

The Black and the White

Half the words below are black; half are white. Place the edge of a mirror on the dotted line above the words and look at the reflection of the words in the mirror. You'll see that the mirror reverses only the black words! Can you explain why?

CHOICE	PURPLE	COOKBOOK	WATER
WAR	DIED	TIGER	ECHO
ICE BOX	SQUARE	BOO HOO	TABLE
TURTLE	HIDE	LARGE	DECIDED
OBOE	ROSE	CHOKED	PIG

Lewis Carroll's Gift

On December 11, 1868, Lewis Carroll wrote the following letter to Dolly Argles, one of his child-friends:

My Dear Dolly,
   . . . I'm going to send your Papa a little present this Christmas, which I daresay you may like to look at. It consists of some thin slices of dried vegetables that somebody has found a way of preparing so that they don't fall to pieces easily. They are marked in a sort of pattern with some chemical stuff or other, and fastened between sheets of pasteboard to preserve them. I believe the *sort* of thing isn't a new invention, but the markings of these are quite new. I inserted them myself. . . .

   No more at present from
           Your loving friend,
             C. L. Dodgson

Dodgson was Lewis Carroll's real name. Can you guess what sort of gift Carroll sent to Dolly's father?

What's the Only Word?

There is one word, and one word only, that can be put inside each of the ten blank rectangles to give ten different meanings to the sentence.

The word must be added only once at a time. For example, if you put the word in the first rectangle, the meaning of the sentence changes. Move the same word to the second rectangle. Again the sentence makes sense, but now it means something still different. The same thing happens with the word in any of the other blanks.

What's the word?

☐ TOM ☐ HELPED ☐

MARY'S ☐ DAUGHTER ☐ CLEAN

☐ MARY'S ☐ PARROT'S ☐

CAGE ☐ YESTERDAY ☐ .

The Vanishing Moustache

Mr. Fulves is standing on the shore of a lake, watching the bathers. In that last picture it looks as if Mr. Fulves' moustache has mysteriously disappeared. Can you explain what happened?

30

The Three Kittens

The owner of this pet shop is trying to persuade two mothers and two daughters, who entered the store together, to buy the three kittens you see playing behind the glass.

He made the sale. Each customer left the store with her own pet kitten. None of them shared a kitten. There were no other kittens in the shop except the three you see here.

How can three kittens be owned by two mothers and two daughters so that each has her own individual pet?

31

Rescuing a Robin

A baby robin, trying to learn to fly, has tumbled
into a hole in a large cement block that is part
of the foundation of a building. The rectangular
hole is just big enough to take a hand and arm,
but it is more than three feet deep. No one can
reach down far enough to pick up the baby bird.
The construction workers don't know what to do.
They're afraid to use long sticks for fear of hurt-
ing the bird.

Susan, who lives nearby, has just thought of a
clever idea. When the men tried it, it worked
beautifully. The robin was rescued unharmed.
One of the men put a ladder against the tree and
returned the baby robin to its nest.

What idea did Susan think of?

SAND

32

The Secret Code

To translate this coded message, read it in a mirror with its edge on the dotted line.

33

The Riders of Inviz

In an earlier puzzle we saw what happened in
Inviz when all the musical instruments became
invisible. The pictures on pp. 54-55 show what
happened on the day that no one could see the
object on which each was riding. What's invisible
in each picture?

34

Rodney's Darts

Rodney has been throwing darts for hours to see if he can score exactly 100. As you see, he's just tossed four darts for a score of 17 + 17 + 17 + 24 = 75 points, but now there is no way he can toss more darts to raise his score to 100.

Can you find a pattern of darts that will add up to exactly 100? You may use as many darts as you like. (Hint: Try first for a score of 50.)

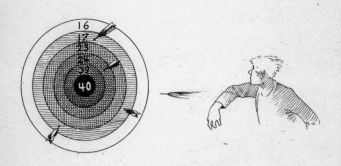

35

More What Do You Say Next?

Here are another dozen catches like the last twelve. The dialogue is between you and a friend. The puzzle is to guess what you say next.

1. YOU: What's the difference between a cow and a pocket calculator?
FRIEND: I give up.
YOU: Your old-age pension.
FRIEND: I don't get it.

2. YOU: What's the sum of 4Q and 6Q?
FRIEND: Ten Q.

3. YOU: It was Hank who taught me that last one.
FRIEND: Hank who?

4. YOU: Would you like to buy a potphur?
FRIEND: What's a potphur?

5. YOU: Did you know that Walter F. Doonton invented doontanite?

FRIEND: What's doontanite?

6. YOU: They're after you! They're after you!
FRIEND: Who?

7. YOU: There's a new joke about a girl who stood on one leg while she sang "The Star Spangled Banner." Have you heard it?
FRIEND: No.

8. YOU: I'm saving up my money to buy a henway.
FRIEND: What's a henway?

9. YOU: I'll bet you a dollar you won't answer "stick of gum" to three questions.
FRIEND: Okay. (Each of you put a dollar on the table.)
YOU: My first question is: "What's your name?"
FRIEND: Stick of gum.
YOU: What's the day of the week?
FRIEND: Stick of gum.

10. YOU: Say the word "two" twice, and then say the word "twain."
FRIEND: Two, two, twain.

11. YOU: Do you eat ice cream with your right or your left hand?

FRIEND: My right hand.

12. YOU: Did you know that people who are smart and beautiful are usually a trifle hard of hearing?

FRIEND: No, I didn't know that.

36

Noah's Ark

The picture shows the animals, two by two, lined up to enter Noah's Ark just before it began to rain. One pair of animals is out of place. Which pair is it?

Ms. Feemster's Message

These four pieces of aluminum sculpture, mounted on a wooden base, are the work of an abstract artist named Elinor Louise Feemster. She is trying to say something. But what?

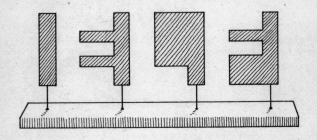

38

The Box Without a Lid

Lewis Carroll is the author of the following puzzle poem:

> John gave his brother James a box:
> About it there were many locks.
>
> James woke and said it gave him pain;
> So he gave it back to John again.
>
> The box was not with lid supplied,
> Yet caused two lids to open wide:
>
> And all these locks had never a key—
> What kind of box, then, could it be?

The Fish That U-turned

This charming toothpick puzzle comes from
Japan. Arrange eight toothpicks to make the fish
shown below. Add a dime for the fish's eye.

The problem: move the dime and just three
toothpicks to make the fish swim in the opposite
direction.

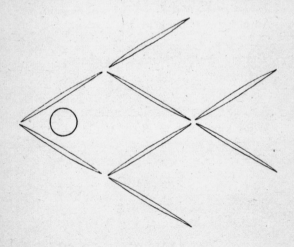

40

A New Angle on
"What's the Difference?"

The artist has drawn the same scene as it would appear at the same moment from two different angles. But he's changed the scene slightly so there are seven spots where things are not the same. (See pp. 66-67). Can you find them?

41

Love and What?

Robert Clark is an artist who changed his last name to Indiana to honor his native state. In 1964 he became famous for his design of the word LOVE. The small picture shows how the word looked on a U.S. postage stamp in 1972.

The large picture is one of Mr. Indiana's aluminum sculptures. It, too, is telling us something in a single word. The puzzle is to guess what the word is.

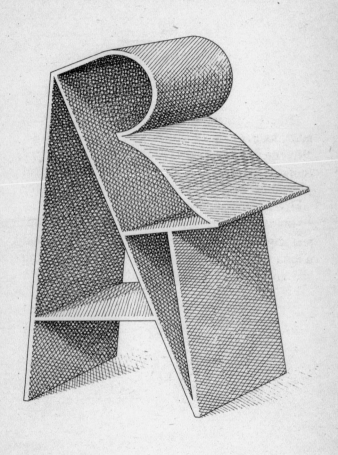

Around to It

Tom Foolery likes to play whimsical jokes on everybody. One day Mr. Foolery said to his wife, "My dear, you're always telling me about the things you'd like to do if you could only get around to it. So I had this made especially for you."

Mr. Foolery handed his wife the circular object shown below. Mrs. Foolery thought about it a long time before she realized what her husband had given her. Can you figure out what it is?

Where Do They Live?

Each person lives in a state that can be spelled by rearranging the letters of that person's name. For example, Roy Kewn lives in New York. Where do the others live?

Roy Kewn
Nora I. Charlton
Colin A. Fair
Dora K. Hatton
Earl Wade
Hilda D. Rosen
A. K. Barnes
J. R. Sweeney

44

The Flatz Beer Goof

Mr. Flatz, owner of the Flatz Beer Company in Milwaukee, decided to paint a slogan on the back of all his beer trucks. The slogan appeared on every truck exactly as shown in the picture.

After a few weeks everybody in Milwaukee was laughing about it. When Mr. Flatz discovered the reason, he had the slogan removed immediately from all the trucks.

Can you figure out why the slogan was so embarrassing to Mr. Flatz?

45

Walking in the Rain

Mr. Brown left his apartment on Main Street, walked east on Main to the barber shop, got a haircut, then walked back home. The eight panels are not in proper sequence. Study them carefully and see if you can put them in the right time sequence. To start you off, the first panel is marked A.

A

75

46

Who Is It?

This marvelous picture was made with a technique developed by scientists at Bell Telephone Laboratories. It is a portrait of a very famous American.

To see who it is, have someone hold the book so you can look at the picture from a distance of 15 or 20 feet.

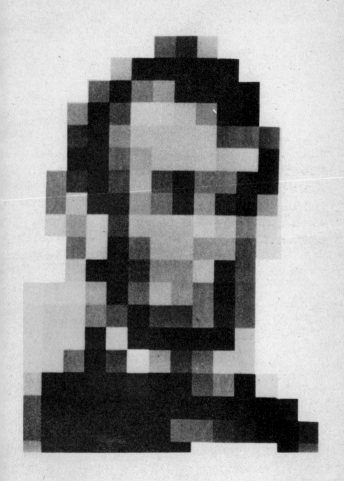

Answers

1
TEN RIDICULOUS RIDDLES

1. It quacks up.
2. A pink carnation.
3. Hold its nose.
4. "Men, get in the boat!"
5. He's a sloppy pizza eater.
6. A Mexican watermelon.
7. At the ghost office.
8. The.
9. A 5,000-pound sandwich that sticks to the roof of your mouth.
10. A mouse going on a long trip.

Square bear
Half Giraffe
Jolly polly
Kickin' chicken

3
"THE WHISTLER"

The Smiths have the painting upside down.
If you turn the page around, you'll see the
whistler. The label is the painting's number.

5
TRICKY QUESTIONS

Speedy Retirement
It was daytime.

Peculiar Word
ISLAND.

Mystery Ball
Toss the ball in the air.

They make ten times as much money.

6

WHAT DO YOU DO NEXT?

---

1. Stick out your tongue and touch your nose with a finger.

2. If your victim says "yes," say, "Then I'll do it again." Do it again and repeat your question: "Did you like that?" If the victim says "no," say, "Then I'll take it back." Do it again, but this time brush your hand over his face from chin to forehead.

3. Write the words "red" and "blue."

4. Pick up his right hand as if it were a telephone, hold its fingers to your ear, and say "Hello."

5. Push your index finger through the cup's handle and give the plate a shove.

6. Bend the match in the center, like a V, before you drop it.

7. Put the newspaper sheet under a door. Have the two people stand on it, but on opposite sides of the door.

8. Put the empty pill bottle on the floor in the center of a room. Go out of the room and crawl back on your hands and knees. You are crawling "in to" the bottle!

9. When your friend extends her palm, smear it with lipstick.

10. Hold a burning match under a glass of water.

11. When the friend gives up, start humming.

12. Just keep quiet and don't do anything.

7

THE MUSICIANS OF INVIZ

The invisible instruments are:
Piano
Flute
Cello
Trombone
Harp
Violin
Cymbals
Drums
Guitar
Clarinet
Conga
Trumpet
(See pp. 84-85).

Baby
Back
Background
Bacon
Badge
Bag
Baggage
Baker
Bakery
Balcony
Bale
Ball
Balustrade
Band
Bananas
Bandage
Banjo
Banner
Barber
Bark
Barn
Barrel
Basin
Basket
Bat
Bellows
Belt
Bench

Bicycle
Billows
Biplane
Bay
Bay window
Beach
Beacon
Beak
Beard
Beast
Bed
Bedroom
Beef
Beets
Beggar
Belfry
Bell
Bird
Blacksmith
Blade
Blanket
Blinders
Blinds
Blindman
Board
Boat
Body
Bonnet

Book	Bridge
Boot	Brook
Bough	Broom
Bow	Brush
Bowl	Bubbles
Bowsprit	Bucket
Box	Buckle
Boy	Buggy
Braces	Buildings
Bracket	Buns
Braid	Bundle
Branch	Buoy
Bread	Bureau
Breeches	Bush
Bricks	Butcher
Bridle	Buttons
Brig	

WHAT'S THE DIFFERENCE?

Circles are drawn around the six spots where the two pictures are not alike.

1. The Christmas message is "Noel" (no L).

2. The letters on the line are formed with straight line segments. Those below the line have curves.

3. Cab, cede, deed, fed, fee, feed, moon, noon, poop, pompon, rust, rusts, rut, ruts, strut, struts, tut, tuts, tut-tut, tut-tuts, tutu (a short skirt that ballerinas wear), tutus. Perhaps you can find some more.

The Two Spirals
The single rope is on the left.

The Curious Cube
The spots show the two right angles on the cube.

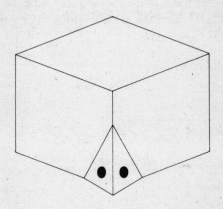

12
DIVIDING THE CAKE

Dad proposed that Henry and his sister flip a coin to see who cuts the cake. Then the person who does *not* cut the cake gets to choose the piece he or she wants.

13
FIND THE MISTAKES

Zipper on door
Upside-down door
Doorknob and lock upside down
Double-barreled shotgun with three barrels
Mouse with squirrel's tail
Shirt on backward
Tie on backward
Hat on backward
Plants growing upside down
Men drinking out of bottom of bottle
Cat with five legs
Fisherman hooks bird
Sails backward
Barn floating on water
Plane flying upside down
Fish in birdcage
Snake with two heads
Upside-down glass of water suspended under the table

Extra finger on a hand
Upside-down umbrella cover
Smoke blowing one way, flag another
No holes in watering-can spout
Upside-down cup handle
Shoes not matching
Title of book on back cover
No trigger on gun
Upside-down drops from watering can

14
THREE MATCH PUZZLES

1. Move one match as shown to make a tiny square hole at the center.

2. Move one match to change the position of the equal sign.

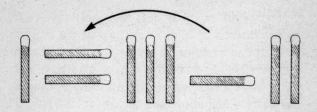

3. To make the equation correct, walk around the table and look at the matches from the other side!

15

HELP SHERLOCK CATCH THE CRIMINALS

The man is standing at the bottom of the picture and is the third person from the left. The woman also is standing in the foreground and is the fifth person from the left.

16
THE TWO WATERING CANS

The small can will hold the most water. Its spigot extends as high as the top of the can, so the can can be filled all the way to the top without overflowing from the spigot. The large can has a short spigot, which will overflow as soon as the can is filled above the spigot.

18
FIND THE DUCK

Give the page a quarter-turn to the left.

19
THREE-LETTER WORD

The Bulgy Balloon

You can prove the balloon is a perfect circle by putting a quarter on top of it.

Two Men on a Cliff

The two cliffs form an "impossible figure" that can't exist in the real world. Cover either side with your hand and everything looks okay, but the entire picture doesn't make sense. Either man can be regarded as on a cliff, but then the other man will be in midair.

Find the Center

The dot on the left is the circle's center.

21

A PAIR OF ANTS

The strip on the left is called a Moebius strip. It has only one side and one edge. In a moment the ants will meet head-on at the bottom of the strip. The other strip is a two-sided surface. Since the ants are on opposite sides, it is impossible for them to meet.

Take two strips of paper and paste the ends together so that they look exactly like the two pictures. Now try to cut each loop in half by cutting along the middle and all the way around. You'll be surprised by what happens!

22
WHAT DO YOU SAY NEXT?

1. "*You're* on the paper."
2. "That's funny. I always thought it was pronounced *Monday*."
3. "You should bathe more often."
4. "You said it."
5. "I'll never give you a letter to mail."
6. "Wouldn't it do more good to put the stamp on the envelope?"
7. "Who do you think you are, Bugs Bunny?"
8. "Paul Revere."
9. "Okay, I'm wrong. Where's the dollar?"
10. "Well, if you don't know where you're going, what are you standing in line for?"
11. "My spine."
12. "Really? How did it taste?"

If you imagine a straight line down the middle of each of the symbols, you'll realize that on the left of each line is a capital letter, and on the right is its mirror reflection. The letters are S, M, T, W, T, F, S—the initials of the days of the week.

Murder at the Ski Resort
The clerk had sold the lawyer a round-trip ticket to Switzerland, and a one-way ticket for his wife.

Funny Business at the Fountain
The lady had the hiccups. Her boss was trying to stop them by frightening her.

Accident on the Thruway
The surgeon was the boy's mother.

26
The Black and the White

The black words are unchanged by the mirror because they are spelled with letters that are unchanged when mirror-reflected and turned upside down. This is not true of the white letters.

27
Lewis Carroll's Gift

The Christmas present was one of Carroll's books.

28
What's the Only Word?

The only word is "only."

29
THE VANISHING MOUSTACHE

Mr. Fulves doesn't have a moustache. What looks like the ends of his moustache in the first three panels are the ends of the canoe he is watching!

30
THE THREE KITTENS

Who said there were *four* ladies? A woman came into the pet shop with her daughter and her granddaughter. That makes two mothers and two daughters!

Susan suggested that sand be poured very slowly, a tiny bit at a time, into the hole. The baby bird moved its feet to stay on top of the sand until the sand brought it up high enough in the hole to be reached.

33
THE RIDERS OF INVIZ

They are riding:
Horse
Bicycle
Canoe
Roller skates
Sled
Skis
Car
Motorcycle
Parachute
Balloon
Airplane
(See pp. 102-103).

The only way to score 50 is with two darts on the 17 ring and one on the 16 ring. Do this twice —four darts on 17 and two on 16—and you will have a score of 100. If you're good at mathematics, you might enjoy proving there is no other way to score 100.

35
MORE WHAT DO YOU SAY NEXT?

1. "You will when you're 65."
2. "You're welcome."
3. "You're welcome."
4. "To cook in."
5. "I dunno. Let's check today's newspaper."
6. "V, W, X, Y, and Z."
7. "You should have. It's our national anthem."
8. "About seven pounds."
9. "Which would you rather have—the two dollars or a stick of gum?"
10. "Good. Now I'll teach you how to say 'airplane.'"
11. "Really? I use a spoon."
12. "Sorry, but I didn't quite hear you."

The animals are supposed to be in alphabetical order: alligators, bears, camels, ducks, elephants, frogs, giraffes, and so on. The frogs are in the wrong spot.

37
MS. FEEMSTER'S MESSAGE

Place sheets of dark paper above and below Ms. Feemster's sculpture. You'll see that it spells her initials, E.L.F.

Lewis Carroll answered his puzzle poem with another poem:

As curlyheaded Jemmy was sleeping in bed,
His brother John gave him a blow on the head;
James opened his eyelids, and spying his brother,
Doubled his fist, and gave him another.
This kind of box, then, is not so rare;
The lids are the eyelids, the locks are the hair,
And so every schoolboy can tell to his cost,
The key to the tangles is constantly lost.

THE FISH THAT U-TURNED

The dime and three toothpicks are moved as shown.

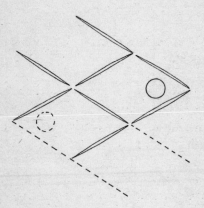

A NEW ANGLE ON "WHAT'S THE DIFFERENCE?"

The circles show the seven spots where things in the two scenes are not the same. (See pp. 108-109).

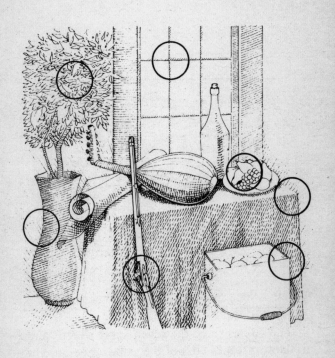

41
Love and What?

The sculpture is a huge monogram of the word ART.

42
Around to It

Tom Foolery gave his wife a "round tuitt." Go back and read what he said, and you'll understand. You can have some fun by making round "tuitts" out of cardboard. Hand them out to friends, telling them you heard they planned to do all sorts of things if they only got *a round tuitt*.

43
WHERE DO THEY LIVE?

Roy Kewn lives in New York; Nora I. Charlton in North Carolina; Colin A. Fair in California; Dora K. Hatton in North Dakota; Earl Wade in Delaware; Hilda D. Rosen in Rhode Island; A. K. Barnes in Nebraska; and J. R. Sweeney in New Jersey.

44
THE FLATZ BEER GOOF

When the doors on the back of the truck were opened, everybody could read a different slogan on the right side!

Walking in the Rain

A. Brown starts out without his umbrella. The sun is shining as he passes the drugstore.

B. The sun is still out when he passes the church.

C. It starts to rain.

D. Brown turns around and goes back for his umbrella.

E. He gets the umbrella, then starts out for the barber shop again. It is raining as he passes the drugstore.

F. It stops raining. The sun comes out and Brown closes his umbrella. He is passing the church.

G. On his way home, after getting his hair cut, it is still not raining as he passes the church.

H. When he reaches the drugstore it has started to rain again, so he opens his umbrella.

29780 PLAY THE LOOK FOR WORDS GAME #1, edited by Ned Webster. Illustrated by Deborah Speed. All you need is a pencil to treat yourself to hours of entertainment with these fifty puzzle games based on such popular themes as the occult, rock groups, sports, movies, and many others. (95¢)

29802 SEA MONSTERS, written and illustrated by Walter Buehr. A fascinating discussion of the myths, facts, and scientific theories about the existence of giant sea creatures from prehistoric times to the present. ($1.25)

29714 THE CURIOUS CLUBHOUSE, by Christine Govan. Illustrated by Leonard Shortall. Seven club members decide to find out just who—or what—is causing all the spooky happenings at their clubhouse. (95¢)

29862 ENCYCLOPEDIA BROWN TAKES THE CASE, by Donald J. Sobol. Illustrated by Leonard Shortall. Join Encyclopedia in his zaniest crime-solving stint, as he foils ten more criminals. ($1.25)

29793 PUNS, GAGS, QUIPS, RIDDLES AND Q's ARE WEIRD O's, by Roy Doty. A collection of rib-tickling riddles and jokes by a well-known author and cartoonist. ($1.25)

(If your bookseller does not have the titles you want, you may order them by sending the retail price, plus 35¢ for postage and handling, to: Mail Service Department, POCKET BOOKS, a Simon & Schuster Division of Gulf & Western Corporation, 1230 Avenue of the Americas, New York, N. Y. 10020. Please enclose check or money order—do not send cash.)

29832